G000100012

For your →

BRILLIANT BIRTHDAY

presents

fun times

Purple Ronnie

summersdale

FOR YOUR BRILLIANT BIRTHDAY

Summersdale Publishers Ltd
46 West Street
Chichester
West Sussex
PO19 1RP
UK

www.summersdale.com

www.purpleronnie.com

Printed and bound in China

ISBN: 978-1-84953-879-4

Substantial discounts on bulk quantities of Summersdale books are available to corporations, professional associations and other organisations. For details contact Nicky Douglas by telephone: +44 (0) 1243 756902, fax: +44 (0) 1243 786300 or email: nicky@summersdale.com.

To.................................

From.............................

Happy Cake Day!

#birthdayledge

Children's party treats

jelly

Adults' party treats

Birthdays are fun
and exciting
You get lots of pressies
and cakes
But mostly it's just
a good reason
To party all night
with your mates!

Here's to a brilliant birthday
You deserve the very best
Time for cake and
giggles and fizz
And then a
well-deserved rest

Bubbles were made
for birthdays!

Ultimate birthday kit:

A whopping great cake!

A soppy and heartfelt birthday card

A party with
mates and
family

A fancy, new,
look-a-million-dollars outfit

The night before
your birthday
Can be a tricky sleep
You start to think
of presents
When you should be
counting sheep!

OMG! Your birthday
is trending!

You on your unbirthday

You on your birthday

It's fair to say
your dancing moves
Are never very risky
But today why not go wild
And score a perfect
10 on Strictly!

I hope all your
wishes come
true (even the
weird ones)!

Everything's better with the word birthday in front of it!

Birthday cake, birthday party, birthday banana...

I've baked two
birthday cakes
To cope with
all your candles
Cos if we lit one per year
That's more than
one cake can handle!

I hope you receive
more gifts
than Zoella has
YouTube hits

Yippee! Your birthday's
here at last
Let's party without
stopping
We'll chug and eat and
drink and feast
Until our belts are popping

Three cheers for
Wonderful Brilliant You
Born *cough* years
ago today
Let's light the candles,
blow the horns
And shout 'HIP HIP HOORAY'

It may be your
special day... but
you're special
all year round

How it feels to receive socks for your birthday when you're a child

How it feels to receive
socks for your birthday
when you're an adult

May your day be full of fun,
Loved ones, cake and laughter
And may you have a painless
Pizza-tastic morning after!

I think you
deserve TEN
birthdays a year!

The polite way to unwrap presents

The BEST way to
unwrap presents

The whole wide world
should stop and bow
Or dip into a curtsey
Because here comes the
champion of champs
And it's their blimmin'
birthday!

May your birthday
have as much choccy
as Easter, as many
presents as Christmas
and as much drink
as New Year's Eve!

The reality

The dream

I hope the birthday
fairy comes
And grants all your
birthday wishes
A unicorn, two
designer handbags
And some sexy
birthday kisses!

MON birthday	TUES birthday	WEDS birthday
THURS birthday	FRI birthday	SAT birthday
SUN birthday		

Let's upgrade to
a birthday WEEK!

Getting out of bed
on an unbirthday

Getting out of bed
on a birthday

You might fancy
movies and popcorn
You might want a
rave-up with mates
Whatever you do on
your birthday
It's sure to be
awesomely great!

Any kind of
birthday cake is
fine, so long as
it's chocolate

Quick! Let off
some streamers
Blow up a few balloons
It's time to dance
and party
To your favourite
birthday 'choons'

Messages and
birthday texts
Can make you smile
and laugh
But proper cards are
best of all
Cos they are made to last

Sometimes
retro is best

**Birthdays mean
extra swag!**

Some people like books
or chocolate
Others are happy with cash
But the best kind of
birthday presents
Are the ones that go
sparkle and flash!

Making birthday memories

Wishing you the best kind of surprises

Good surprise - a gorgeous kissogram

You might be one
year older
But there's no point
feeling blue
Because you look amazing
The same (young)
gorgeous you!

Just the one drink!

Birthday Tip 1

Try to look happy when you open a present...

... Even if it's a bit rubbish

Make sure you take
lots of selfies
And give us your best
birthday grin
Just remember to
never look down
Or you'll end up with
two double chins!

Don't let ANYTHING
rain on your birthday
(not even rain)

Birthday Tip 2

**Relaxing is the rule
on your birthday...**

... You can even leave
your pants on the floor

Your birthday is
the best excuse
To shout some
facts out loud
Fact one: you're
flippin' awesome
And you stand out
from the crowd

I think your
birthday should be
a national holiday!

It's sure to be spectacular
A guaranteed big hit
This birthday will
be wonderful
Cos you're the star of it!

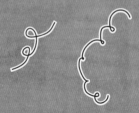

coolabi

If you're interested in finding out more
about our books, find us on Facebook
at **Summersdale Publishers** and follow
us on Twitter at **@Summersdale**.

www.summersdale.com